Prelude in C min

BWV 999

A:1

Bach
(1685–1750)

This Prelude was probably composed during the period 1717–23 when Johann Sebastian Bach was *Capellmeister* (director of music) at the court of Prince Leopold of Anhalt-Cöthen. It is an arpeggiated prelude; that is, it consists of a series of chords, all of which are arpeggiated according to the same pattern. Most of Bach's arpeggiated preludes were composed for keyboard instruments. The Prelude in C minor, however, was originally written for the lute, but works equally well when played on a keyboard.

The harmonic structure of the piece is built on pedal points: tonic pedal in C minor (bars 1–7); then, after a transition (bars 7–16), dominant pedal in G minor (bars 17–32), which then becomes a tonic pedal in G minor (bars 33–43). So, unusually for Bach, it ends in the overall dominant, G minor, though with a *Tierce de Picardie* (major 3rd in the last chord). At the third crotchet of every bar, the arpeggiated pattern requires an alternation between right hand and left hand; in other words, the left-hand quavers need to be shortened to semiquavers.

Source: MS copy, 'Praelude in C mol [sic] pour la Lute', in the hand of J. P. Kellner, Staatsbibliothek zu Berlin, Preussischer Kulturbesitz, Mus. ms. Bach P 804, pp. 101–3. This copy is quite inaccurate, and obvious errors have been corrected without notice. Kellner gives the first bass note of bar 23 as *E*(♭) – a highly unlikely reading in view of the *D* pedal that prevails from bars 17–32. The reading *D* is restored here, as it is also in the *Neue Bach-Ausgabe* V/10 (pp. 122–3). All the dynamics and the *rit.* in the penultimate bar are editorial suggestions only. The last chord is written as a crotchet in the source.

4

Piano Exam Pieces

ABRSM Grade 4

Selected from the 2021 & 2022 syllabus

Name

Date of exam

Contents

page

Editor for ABRSM: Richard Jones

Other pieces for Grade 4

Published in 2020 by ABRSM (Publishing) Ltd, a wholly owned subsidiary of ABRSM, 4 London Wall Place, London EC2Y 5AU, United Kingdom
© 2020 by The Associated Board of the Royal Schools of Music
Distributed worldwide by Oxford University Press

Music origination by Julia Bovee
Cover by Kate Benjamin & Andy Potts, with thanks to Brighton College
Printed in England by Caligraving Ltd, Thetford, Norfolk, on materials from sustainable sources.
P14983

Etude in A minor

No. 3 from *30 Children's Pieces*, Op. 27

D. B. Kabalevsky
(1904–87)

The Russian composer Dmitry Borisovich Kabalevsky studied piano and composition at the Moscow Conservatory, where he later taught, being appointed professor in 1939. He was active in the field of music education and wrote many works for young people, including the *30 Children's Pieces*, Op. 27.

In his performance notes to the Boosey & Hawkes edition, John York has characterised the piece as follows: it is 'a well-known study that develops a sense of dramatic dynamic shaping, neat left-hand slurring and brilliant right-hand fingerwork. It should have a sense of urgency but not of unsteadiness.'

© Copyright 1938 by Boosey & Hawkes Music Publishers Ltd for the United Kingdom and Republic of Ireland
Reproduced by permission of Boosey & Hawkes Music Publishers Ltd.

A:3

Minuet and Trio

D. 41 No. 21

Franz Schubert
(1797–1828)

The Austrian composer Franz Schubert wrote many keyboard dances – Deutsche, Ländler, minuets, waltzes etc. – which often have the character of written-down improvisations. According to his biographer Alfred Einstein, 'This must have been the way he played when he provided music for his friends to dance to at parties.' The *30 Menuette mit Trios* (30 Minuets with Trios), D. 41, 10 of which are now lost, date from 1813 when Schubert was only 16 years old.

Both the Minuet and Trio have repeated notes over a moving bass in their first bar. In other respects, however, the two dances are very different from each other. The Minuet is relatively plain, though spiced up with dotted rhythms, whereas the Trio is more decorative and playful, with its short semiquaver trill figures and runs. Also, Schubert plays a trick on us in the second phrase of the Trio (bars 21–3): every other phrase is four bars long, but this one is only three bars.

Source: first edition, *Franz Schubert's Werke*, Series 12: No. 18 from *Zwanzig Menuette* (Leipzig: Breitkopf & Härtel, 1889). Slurs analogous to Schubert's have been added by the editor. All dynamics are editorial suggestions only, except the **pp** at the start of the Trio, which is present in the source. The e' in bar 23 is a minim in the source; it has been altered here to a crotchet in accordance with bar 31.

Trio

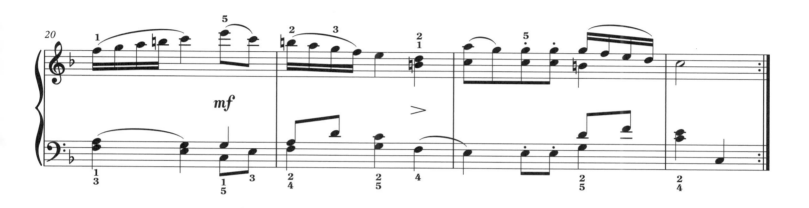

Minuet D.C. al Fine

B:1

Moonbeams

No. 1 from *Rendezvous with Midnight*

Barbara Arens
(born 1960)

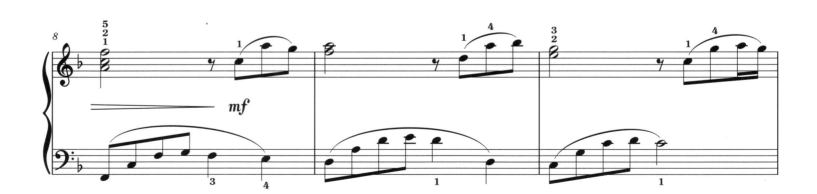

Barbara Arens studied at the Mozarteum in Salzburg, Austria, from the age of 13. She was a concert performer, mainly on harpsichord and organ, but now specialises in piano teaching and in composing piano pieces for her pupils.

'Moonbeams' is the opening piece in the collection *Rendezvous with Midnight: 12 + 1 Nocturnes for Teens*. It is prefaced by a verse by William Blake: 'The moon, like a flower, / In heaven's high bower, / With silent delight / Sits and smiles on the night'. The direction '*con Ped.*' is editorial.

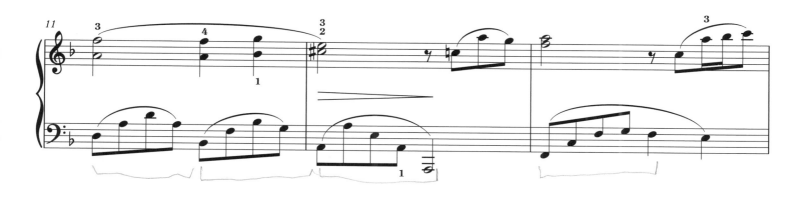

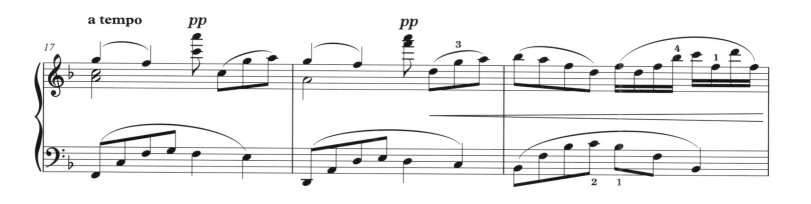

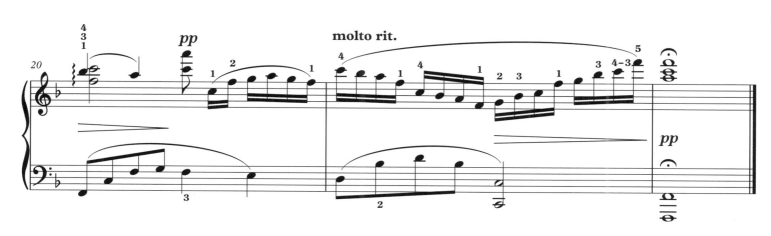

B:2

Miniature Pastoral

No. 2 from *Three Miniature Pastorals*, Set 1

Frank Bridge
(1879–1941)

The English composer Frank Bridge studied composition with Charles Stanford at the Royal College of Music in London. He also played viola in the Joachim Quartet and the English String Quartet, and conducted at the Savoy Theatre and at Covent Garden. His early works were written in a late Romantic style, but later he was strongly influenced by the music of Alban Berg. In the late 1920s he taught the young Benjamin Britten, who then championed his teacher's music. One of Britten's first major successes was his *Variations on a Theme of Frank Bridge* of 1937.

This piece is the second of six *Miniature Pastorals* composed in 1917 and published in two sets. Written in the style of a waltz, it features a long-note theme alternating between the hands (bars 1–16) and a chromatic descent in both hands, first slow (bars 17–24), then fast (bars 29–36). A variant of the original theme returns in bars 37–52, followed by a coda.

The original edition has pedal marks only in the coda (bars 53–62); pedal marks before that are editorial.

B:3

Erster Verlust

No. 16 from *Album für die Jugend*, Op. 68

Robert Schumann
(1810–56)

Robert Schumann's *Album für die Jugend* (Album for the Young) was composed in less than a month in 1848. At the time, the composer wrote: 'I don't remember ever having been in such good musical form … the pieces simply poured out, one after another.' Some of the 42 pieces in the collection were dedicated to Schumann's daughter Marie on her seventh birthday.

'Erster Verlust' (First Loss) is essentially a lyrical piece with the melody in the right hand, but the sense of loss is intensified in bars 21–5, where the opening of the theme enters four times in *stretto* (overlapping entries).

Source: *43* [sic] *Clavierstücke für die Jugend*, Op. 68 (Hamburg: Schuberth & Co., 1850)

Etwas langsamer
[somewhat slower]

Im Tempo

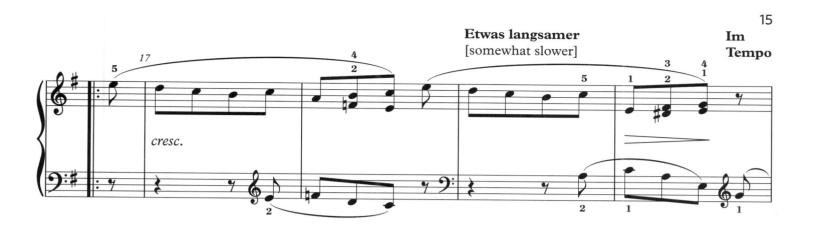

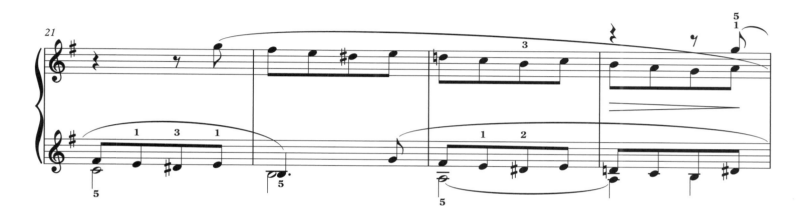

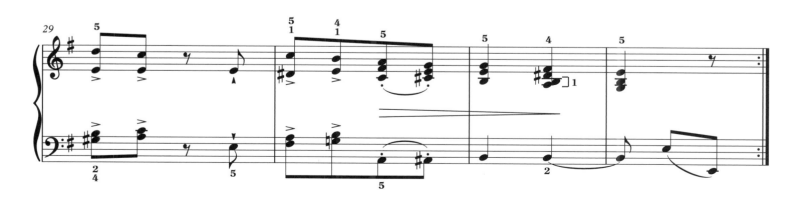

C:1

Teasing Song

No. 18 from *For Children*, Vol. 2

Béla Bartók
(1881–1945)

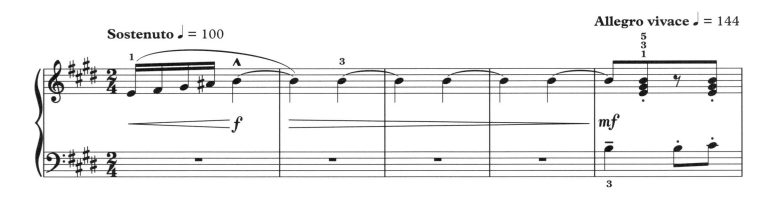

The Hungarian composer Béla Bartók wrote *For Children* between 1908 and 1910. It was his first large collection of folksong arrangements, and contains both Hungarian and Slovakian tunes. The composer's aim was to reveal 'the simple and non-Romantic beauties of folk music' to young pianists. He revised the collection in 1943.

'Teasing Song' is taken from Volume 2 of the revised version, which is based on Slovakian folk tunes. In this piece, the folk melody is played three times: first, in the left hand and in the tonic E major (bars 5–16); second time, in the right hand and in the dominant B major (bars 17–28); and third time, in the left hand with the first half in G major and the second half in the tonic (bars 29–40). Although the composer's metronome mark from bar 5 onwards is ♩ = 144, students may prefer a slower tempo, for example ♩ = c.132.

I Hear What You Say

No. 4 from *Cool Beans!*, Vol. 1

Ben Crosland
(born 1968)

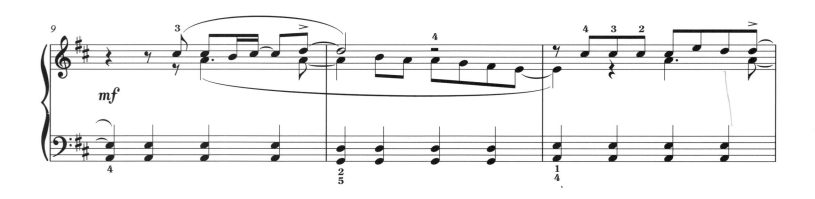

As a teenager, Ben Crosland developed a strong interest in composition, and since then he has experimented with a variety of compositional genres. Having begun his teaching career in 1987, he now enjoys writing educational music for his piano students, mostly in jazz and popular styles. He runs a music school, called The Music Grove, in his home town of Worcester, England.

This piece is taken from *Cool Beans!*, Volume 1: *Dreams, Themes and Love Songs*, which contains 12 pieces written in nostalgic, romantic styles. 'I Hear What You Say' consists of a four-phrase melody (bars 1–12), which is then repeated in a lightly varied form (bars 13–24), followed by a brief coda.

© 2019 Editions Musica Ferrum Ltd
Printed with permission of Editions Musica Ferrum: info@musica-ferrum.com

Shark Soup

from *Sam Wedgwood's Project*, Book 2

Sam Wedgwood
(born 1980)

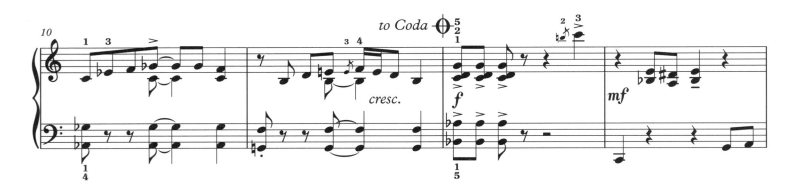

Sam Wedgwood is an English composer who writes for international TV, advertising and film. He has also composed several books of piano music. He studied music at the Royal Academy of Music in London and, in his early career, toured as a multi-instrumentalist in jazz artist Jamie Cullum's band. He now lives in Australia and is committed to the promotion of music education, acting as a freelance consultant in several schools.

'Shark Soup' is selected from Wedgwood's *Project*, Book 2, which is devoted to jazz piano pieces.